The Official
West Ham United
Football Club
Annual 2008

Written By Danny Francis

A Grange Publication

© 2007. Published by Grange Communications Ltd., Edinburgh,
under licence from West Ham United Football Club.
Printed in the EU.

ISBN 978-1-905426-96-6

Photographs © Griffiths Photographers

£6.99

CONTENTS

Welcome to the West Ham United Annual 2008!

We hope you enjoy looking back over an eventful 2006-07 season, and ahead to what is promising to be an exciting new 2007-08 campaign, with Alan Curbishley hoping to lead his new-look squad back to where they belong – in the top half of the Barclays Premier League!

After his team avoided relegation from the top flight with a memorable 1-0 win over Champions Manchester United at Old Trafford on the final day of last season, the Hammers boss made several exciting new changes in the summer months, bringing in the likes of Scott Parker, Julien Faubert, Craig Bellamy and Freddie Ljungberg.

In the following pages, we reflect on the unforgettable 2006-07 season, including the top ten goals of the campaign and all the vital statistics, focus on the manager, the new signings, and the young starlets hoping to make a first team breakthrough in the near future.

We also have an in-depth, exclusive interview with returning Hammers hero Dean Ashton – back in action after a year on the sidelines through injury – while there are quizzes, a wordsearch and some fantastic pictures to illustrate your Upton Park heroes in all their glory!

So enjoy the West Ham United 2008 Annual, and keep cheering the Hammers on!

> **"** The results picked up alongside the confidence and it just goes to show what can be achieved. **"**

ALAN CURBISHLEY

When he left West Ham United in July 1979, 21-year-old Alan Curbishley surely never dreamed that he would return as manager one day. But 27 years on, Curbs was chairman Eggert Magnusson's Number One choice to step into the Upton Park dug-out, when Alan Pardew left last December.

By then, the Forest Gate-born, Canning Town-raised, midfielder had become one of the most respected managers in the game following a miracle-working 15 years at Charlton Athletic, which culminated in an interview to follow Sven-Goran Eriksson into the England job. And thankfully Curbs had no hesitation accepting the Chairman's challenge to steer Hammers clear of relegation.

As a player, the hugely-talented England U-21 international would have waltzed into most sides. However, his path to the Hammers' midfield had been blocked by the likes of legends such as Trevor Brooking, Billy Bonds and Alan Devonshire. And that meant that the local lad, who joined West Ham as a 13-year-old schoolboy, had to go in search of first-team football away from Upton Park, where he had made 95 appearances, scoring five goals.

After joining Birmingham City, Curbs then moved to Aston Villa, Charlton Athletic and Brighton & Hove Albion. Returning to Charlton as player-coach in 1990, he then became joint-manager with team-mate Steve Gritt a few months later.

In 1995, Curbs assumed sole control of the Addicks and duly transformed the cash-strapped south Londoners into an established Premiership side.

That interview for the England post followed but after 15 years in charge at The Valley, he then decided to take a well-earned break from the game.

Both the nation's loss and Charlton's loss were soon to become West Ham's gain when Eggert Magnusson asked Curbs to become the club's 11th manager following Alan Pardew's departure in December 2006.

Following in the footsteps of Syd King, Ted Fenton, John Lyall, Billy Bonds and Harry Redknapp, he became the sixth manager to have also played for the club. With former Hammers' team-mate, Mervyn Day, alongside him on the bench, Alan did not have to be told anything about West Ham United's rich and proud tradition for playing football the way it should be played.

Indeed, he could not have had a better start when he kicked off with a whirlwind win over champions-elect Manchester United and a gritty draw at Fulham. But despite bringing Lucas Neill, Luis Boa Morte, Calum Davenport, Nigel Quashie, Matthew Upson and Kepa Blanco to the club in January, Curbs still had to draw on all his experience as he subsequently found himself at the bottom of the Premiership, ten points adrift of safety with just nine games remaining.

"We haven't given up the fight," he insisted. "We just need lift-off."

Sure enough, as every week passed, Curbs' influence started to show through, while the likes of Neill brought new-found discipline and leadership out onto the field, where Carlos Tevez's goals were proving to be priceless.

Victory at Blackburn Rovers in mid-March boosted confidence ahead of a win over Middlesbrough and an epic three-pointer at the Emirates Stadium, where Arsenal suffered their first-ever defeat at their new home. By the time that seven-goal Tevez had collected his richly deserved Hammer of the Year award before the win over Bolton Wanderers, Curbs had also inspired his team to equally magnificent victories over Everton and Wigan Athletic.

The in-form Hammers were simply sweeping everyone aside and when the Argentinian ace struck the vital goal at Old Trafford on the final day of the season to give Curbs his second victory over Manchester United, that made it seven wins from the final nine games.

"It had been difficult coming into the club in mid-season," reveals the modest Curbs. "You just couldn't see where another result was coming from but, all along, people were telling me that if we could only pick up a couple of results, then I'd see the difference in the players and that's exactly what happened. All I've done is kept things low key and the training simple. The results picked up alongside the confidence and it just goes to show what can be achieved."

Hammer of the Year 2006-07
CARLOS TEVEZ

There was only ever going to be one winner of the 2007 Hammer of the Year award. Step forward Carlitos 'Carlos' Tevez!

The Argentinian ace had already shown just what he could do at World Cup 2006. And when Hammers signed him alongside fellow countryman, Javier Mascherano on transfer deadline day just a few weeks later, Planet Football looked on with envy.

Just like Chelsea's £30million, Andriy Shevchenko, the 22-year-old goal-getter needed time to adapt to the hustle and bustle of the pacy Premiership.

But by the end of the season, there was absolutely no doubting who the East Enders would rather have in their ranks.

Sure, the South American striker took time to find his feet on English soil and in the early days he could not score a goal for all the T-bone steaks in Argentina.

But the tough, teasing, tricky Tevez had still produced enough flicks and tricks to convince the Hammers' supporters that he was the man to guide their team to safety.

"He hasn't scored any goals," argued Alan Curbishley, when he first took over.

"Just give him some games and he'll find the net," replied the fans who had taken the boy from the big, bad backstreets of Fuerte Apache in Buenos Aires to their hearts.

And after overcoming the disappointment of seeing Mascherano move to Liverpool in January, Tevez quickly set about repaying Curbs for finally giving him his chance.

A scintillating free-kick in the heartbreaking defeat against Tottenham Hotspur saw the shirt-less striker dive into the crowd as he memorably celebrated with his loyal fans, who had finally been rewarded with a long-overdue goal.

That strike unlocked an avalanche of net-busters as the former Boca Juniors and Corinthians striker struck seven times in Hammers last ten matches.

Ignoring all the off-field controversy, Carlos was only worried about doing the business out on the pitch.

Battling with the heart of a lion, he scored against Blackburn Rovers, Middlesbrough, and Chelsea before hitting a destructive double in the penultimate match against Bolton Wanderers.

By then, it was probably already written in the script that, against all odds, saviour Tevez would net the crucial winner at Manchester United on a nail-biting Survival Sunday, to keep West Ham in the Premiership this season.

Make no mistake, Carlos Tevez can always be guaranteed a hero's reception whenever he steps out at Upton Park.

Meanwhile, fellow new-signings Lucas Neill and Robert Green plus claret and blue blooded Mark Noble each had claims to the runners-up spot.

But in the end, it was another local lad, top-scorer, Bobby Zamora (pictured below), who deservedly claimed the prize thanks to his 11-goal haul, including that wonderful winner at Arsenal.

Bobby Zamora

Season Review
August 2006

12th   A week before the start of the new Premier League campaign, Hammers hold Greek champions Olympiakos to a 1-1 draw in a prestige pre-season friendly at Upton Park, with Marlon Harewood netting and Dean Ashton impressing in front of new England manager Steve McClaren.

15th   Disaster strikes as Ashton, having been called into the full England squad for the first time ahead of a friendly against Greece, sustains a badly broken ankle while training with his international team-mates. Initial reports suggest that the striker will be ruled out for up to four months.

19th   Hammers kick off the 2006-07 Premiership campaign where they left off last season, with an impressive victory at Upton Park. After Darren Bent's penalty earns a 1-0 lead for Charlton – now managed by former Hammer Iain Dowie following Alan Curbishley's departure – two goals from Bobby Zamora and a last-minute strike from Carlton Cole turn things around to secure a comfortable 3-1 victory.

22nd   In the first away game of the season, newly-promoted Watford hold Hammers to a 1-1 draw at Vicarage Road. Zamora is again on the scoresheet, cancelling out Marlon King's opener to make it an unbeaten start for Alan Pardew's men.

26th   Without a win at Anfield in almost 43 years, Hammers look set to break the Liverpool hoodoo when Zamora nets his fourth goal in three games with a fortunate cross-shot that beats Reina at his near post. However, two goals in the space of three minutes just before half-time, from Daniel Agger and Peter Crouch, turn the game on its head and inflict our first defeat of the season.

31st   Transfer deadline day, and West Ham United becomes the focus of the football world as Argentinian international stars Carlos Tevez and Javier Mascherano arrive at Upton Park in a move from Brazilian side Corinthians, a deal arranged by their former owner Kia Joorabchian, who just 24 hours later announces his intention to launch a takeover bid at the Boleyn Ground.

September 2006

10th After an exciting 11-day wait for their first glimpse of new Argentinian duo Carlos Tevez and Javier Mascherano in action, Hammers fans were forced to wait a bit longer as the pair were named as substitutes for the visit of Aston Villa in front of the live Sky TV cameras. And after Liam Ridgewell's fourth-minute opener had given Villa the lead, it was that man Zamora who stole the headlines again, with his fifth goal of the season to equalise. Tevez arrived to a rapturous reception in the 61st minute, but Alan Pardew's men were forced to settle for a point.

14th Hammers endure disappointment in their return to European football, as in-form Italian side Palermo snatch a 1-0 victory at Upton Park in the UEFA Cup first round, first leg tie. Both Tevez and Mascherano make their first starts, but Caracciolo's 45th-minute strike leaves the Londoners with a mountain to climb.

17th The disappointment continues, as Newcastle United – led by former Hammers boss Glenn Roeder – grab a 2-0 victory at Upton Park, thanks to goals from Damien Duff and Obafemi Martins.

23rd Striker Georgios Samaras makes it a Greek tragedy for Hammers, as he nets twice at the City of Manchester Stadium to secure a 2-0 win for Stuart Pearce's men and leave the dejected visitors without a win since the opening day of the season.

28th The European dream is ended as quickly as it began, with a 3-0 second leg defeat against Palermo in Sicily. Two goals from Simplicio and one from Di Michele make it a 4-0 aggregate defeat for Hammers in the UEFA Cup first round.

October 2006

1st   October sadly begins in the same way that September finished, as Hammers slump to another defeat, this time against Premiership new-boys Reading at Upton Park. A long-range strike from Seol in the second minute is enough to give Steve Coppell's men all three points, leaving the hosts without a win – or a goal – in five matches.

14th   The goalless and winless run continues, as this time it is former Hammers boss Harry Redknapp who comes back to haunt his old side, leading Portsmouth to a 2-0 win at Fratton Park – Kanu and Andy Cole grabbing the goals.

22nd   A London derby at White Hart Lane whets the appetite and gives Hammers fans hope that a revival in fortunes can begin in the best way possible. However, a goal on the stroke of half-time from Egyptian striker Mido is enough to secure all three points for Spurs.

24th   In the Carling Cup second round tie at League One side Chesterfield, Marlon Harewood's early strike finally ends the drought in front of goal. However, the lower league outfit battle back bravely and, after Colin Larkin's 54th minute equaliser, Caleb Folan hits a late winner to knock Hammers out of the competition.

29th   The pressure is on as Hammers return to Upton Park for a crucial Premiership clash against Blackburn Rovers. An early goal from Teddy Sheringham settles the nerves and Hayden Mullins' header with 10 minutes remaining leads to a surge of relief all around Upton Park. David Bentley's late strike is thankfully only a consolation, as Alan Pardew's men finally bring their barren run to an end.

November 2006

5th The revival appears to be on, as Hammers secure a memorable 1-0 home win against Arsenal thanks to Marlon Harewood's late strike, which leads to a few fireworks between Alan Pardew and Arsene Wenger down in the technical area.

11th Hammers fail to build on their two recent home victories, as a scrappy affair against Middlesbrough at the Riverside Stadium ends with Italian striker Massimo Maccarone grabbing a late winner.

18th Hammers come close to snatching a point against reigning champions Chelsea with a brave display at Stamford Bridge, but end up on the losing side again as Geremi's free-kick on the stroke of half-time separates the two sides.

21st West Ham United confirm that an £85million takeover bid from an Icelandic consortium led by Eggert Magnusson has been accepted, marking the end of Terence Brown's reign as Chairman after 14 years at the helm.

25th Magnusson arrives at Upton Park to a hero's welcome and enjoys a perfect start to his leadership of the Club as a goal from midfielder Hayden Mullins secures a vital 1-0 victory against fellow Premiership strugglers Sheffield United.

December 2006

3rd Despite three successive home victories, Hammers just can't find similar form on their travels, as this time Everton leave them still searching for their first away win of the season. Second half goals from Leon Osman and James Vaughan seal a 2-0 defeat as a concerned Eggert Magnusson looks on.

6th Three days later the home form begins to slump, too, as Wigan Athletic snatch a 2-0 victory at Upton Park, thanks to goals from David Cotterill and Leighton Baines.

9th A dismal evening at the Reebok Stadium, as a toothless Hammers side are on the wrong end of a 4-0 thrashing against Bolton Wanderers. Two goals from Kevin Davies, plus one each from El Hadji Diouf and Nicolas Anelka secure the points for Sam Allardyce's men, as the pressure increases on Alan Pardew.

11th The pressure finally takes its toll, as West Ham United announce the departure of their manager after three years in charge. Concerned by the performances of recent weeks, Chairman Eggert Magnusson reveals his wish to appoint a new boss before the January transfer window opens.

13th The search doesn't take long, as overwhelming favourite and former Hammers midfielder Alan Curbishley is appointed as the manager of West Ham United after ending a successful 15-year reign at Charlton Athletic earlier in the year. Appointing his close friend and also former Upton Park team-mate, Mervyn Day, as his assistant, Curbs admits that his love for the Club made it an offer he couldn't refuse.

17th A new era at West Ham United gets off to the best possible start, as Nigel Reo-Coker's late goal seals a memorable 1-0 victory against league leaders Manchester United at Upton Park.

23rd Displaying what appears to be a new-found sense of belief and confidence, Hammers battle to a hard-fought 0-0 draw against Fulham at Craven Cottage, although Paul Konchesky's harsh late sending-off overshadows a decent point.

26th The honeymoon period is over for Alan Curbishley, as Hammers are hit by a sucker punch on Boxing Day – heavyweight defender Linvoy Primus landing two knock-out blows to seal a 2-1 win for Harry Redknapp's Portsmouth side.

30th 2006 ends in further disappointment for Hammers, as a late strike from American striker DaMarcus Beasley gives Manchester City a 1-0 win to make it two defeats in four days at Upton Park for Curbishley's men.

January 2007

1st If 2006 ended in disappointment, then 2007 begins in disaster, as Hammers fans are subjected to a New Year's Day nightmare at the Madejski Stadium, watching their team suffer a humiliating 6-0 defeat against Reading, whose hunger and determination as a newly-promoted Premiership side is exactly what appears to be missing from some Hammers stars presently.

5th With the January transfer window now open, Alan Curbishley makes Fulham winger Luis Boa Morte his first signing as West Ham United manager, snapping up the Portuguese international on a three-and-a-half year contract.

6th A brief respite from the strains and stresses of Premiership life, as League One side Brighton and Hove Albion are the visitors to Upton Park for an FA Cup third round tie and leave empty-handed – goals from young midfielder Mark Noble, Carlton Cole and Hayden Mullins securing a 3-0 win and safe passage to the fourth round.

8th Experienced midfielder Nigel Quashie becomes the next new arrival, signing from West Bromwich Albion for a fee of £1.5million.

13th In a dramatic encounter at Upton Park, a late equaliser from French defender Phillipe Cristanval leaves Hammers stunned, as Fulham snatch a 3-3 draw. A double strike from Yossi Benayoun and one from Bobby Zamora looked to have secured a vital first Premiership win of 2007 for Alan Curbishley but, after Zamora is dismissed for two bookable offences, 10-man Hammers fail to hold on.

18th Defender Calum Davenport, who spent a loan spell at Upton Park in September 2004, completes a permanent move to the Hammers from Tottenham Hotspur.

20th Hammers are again forced to settle for a point despite deserving all three, as an early 2-0 lead against Newcastle United at St James' Park – thanks to goals from Carlton Cole and Marlon Harewood – is wiped out by a controversial equaliser from James Milner and a penalty from Nobby Solano.

22nd Australian international captain Lucas Neill becomes Alan Curbishley's fourth signing in the January transfer window, completing a move from Blackburn Rovers after turning down the attentions of Liverpool in favour of joining Eggert Magnusson on his dream for the future at Upton Park.

24th Spanish striker Kepa Blanco signs on loan from Sevilla until the end of the season.

27th Relegation certainties Watford visit Upton Park in the FA Cup fourth round, and pull off a shock 1-0 victory, as Anthony McNamee's acrobatic finish sees the Hornets through to the last 16. Of more concern to Curbs is an injury to new-boy Neill, who limps off with an ankle injury just 47 minutes into his Hammers debut.

30th Kepa steps off the bench to net a debut goal against Liverpool at Upton Park, but it isn't enough to stop the Reds taking all three points thanks to two quickfire goals from Peter Crouch and Dirk Kuyt.

31st England international defender Matthew Upson becomes the sixth and final signing in the January transfer window, sealing a £6million move from Birmingham City.

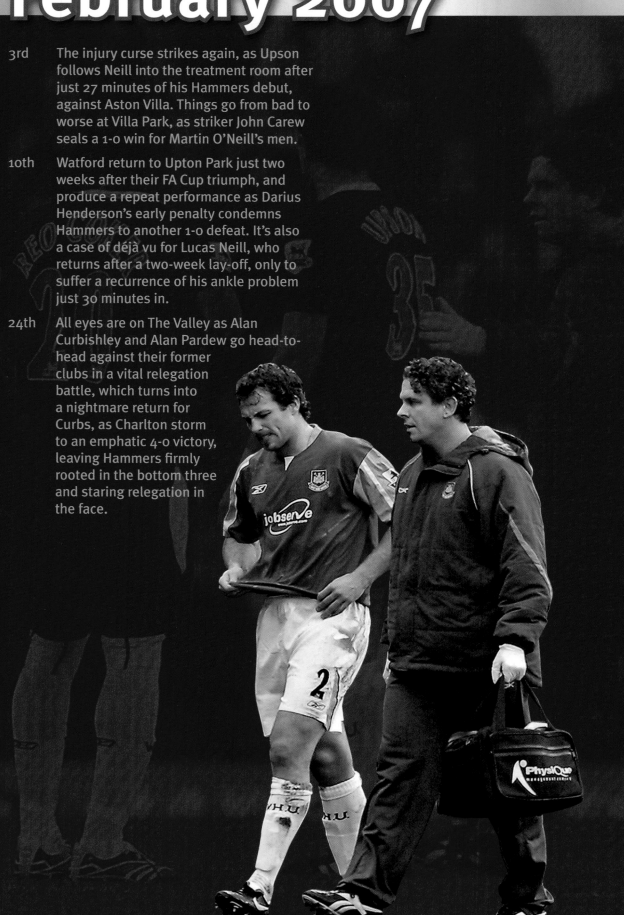

February 2007

3rd The injury curse strikes again, as Upson follows Neill into the treatment room after just 27 minutes of his Hammers debut, against Aston Villa. Things go from bad to worse at Villa Park, as striker John Carew seals a 1-0 win for Martin O'Neill's men.

10th Watford return to Upton Park just two weeks after their FA Cup triumph, and produce a repeat performance as Darius Henderson's early penalty condemns Hammers to another 1-0 defeat. It's also a case of déjà vu for Lucas Neill, who returns after a two-week lay-off, only to suffer a recurrence of his ankle problem just 30 minutes in.

24th All eyes are on The Valley as Alan Curbishley and Alan Pardew go head-to-head against their former clubs in a vital relegation battle, which turns into a nightmare return for Curbs, as Charlton storm to an emphatic 4-0 victory, leaving Hammers firmly rooted in the bottom three and staring relegation in the face.

March 2007

4th With his team rooted to the bottom of the Premiership table, Alan Curbishley rings the changes for the visit of arch rivals Tottenham Hotspur to Upton Park. Lucas Neill and Matthew Upson make welcome returns from injury, while young Mark Noble is recalled to the starting line-up for the first time since January. However, the injury curse strikes again just 10 minutes in, as Upson limps off with a recurrence of his calf problem. The groans soon turn to cheers, though, when Noble fires Hammers into the lead, and the roof is almost lifted off Upton Park as Carlos Tevez finally nets his long-awaited first goal for the Club – an exquisite free-kick – to give his side a 2-0 half-time lead. At half-time, Curbs urges his players to keep things solid for the first 10 minutes of the second half, only to see Jermain Defoe pull one back from the penalty spot and then Teemu Tainio equalise from the penalty spot. Hammers again show great character, though, and when Bobby Zamora heads home with just five minutes remaining, the vital three points look to be in the bag.

17th Hammers travel to Blackburn Rovers knowing that a win is vital to keep alive their slim hopes of survival but, when defender Christopher Samba heads the home team into an early second half lead, another defeat looks likely. Suddenly, though, Hammers somehow produce a stirring revival and, after Carlos Tevez equalises from the penalty spot, an amazing goalmouth scramble leads to Bobby Zamora poking the ball goalwards, with a linesman's raised flag signalling a winning goal for the visitors. TV replays later prove the ball didn't cross the line, but boss Alan Curbishley admits he'll accept the stroke of luck!

31st Middlesbrough are the visitors to Upton Park and leave empty-handed as early strikes from Zamora and Tevez again make it two wins in a row for Hammers to keep the survival dream just about alive.

April 2007

7th After becoming the last team to win a Premiership match at Highbury in February 2006, Hammers also become the first team to win a Premiership match at the new Emirates Stadium, securing an amazing league double over Arsenal. Bobby Zamora's expertly-taken goal on the stroke of half-time is enough to seal a crucial three points for Alan Curbishley's men, who have a stunning performance from goalkeeper Rob Green to thank for keeping the Gunners at bay.

14th Hammers travel north to face Sheffield United in a vital relegation battle full of confidence after three victories on the spin and a memorable display against Arsenal last week. However, the revival looks to be over as Neil Warnock's men pull off a painful 3-0 victory with goals from Michael Tonge, Phil Jagielka and Jon Stead leaving shell-shocked Hammers facing a mountain to climb.

18th Champions Chelsea are in town and, when Carlos Tevez produces a wonder-strike to cancel out Shaun Wright-Phillips' early goal, it looks as though Hammers might be about to pull off another shock result. However, Wright-Phillips doubles his tally and the Blues step up a gear to add further goals from

Kalou and Drogba and condemn the hosts to a 4-1 defeat.

21st With just four Premiership matches remaining, Alan Curbishley admits that his side need to win the majority of them if they are to escape relegation. A superb early goal from Bobby Zamora is enough to see off Everton at Upton Park in the penultimate home game of the season.

28th Just 24 hours after the Club are fined £5.5million by an Independent Inquiry for breaching Premier League rules over the signing of Argentine duo Javier Mascherano and Carlos Tevez, Hammers head to the JJB Stadium to face Wigan Athletic in another mouth-watering relegation battle. Luis Boa Morte's first goal for the Club sets the visitors on their way, and second half strikes from Yossi Benayoun and Marlon Harewood seal a 3-0 win to have the fantastic travelling Hammers fans singing all the way home.

May 2007

5th In their final home match of the season, Hammers make it three wins in a row and lift themselves out of the bottom three for the first time since Alan Curbishley's arrival in December, with a stunning 3-1 victory against Bolton Wanderers. New Hammer of the Year Carlos Tevez is the architect, scoring the first two and creating a wonderful third for Mark Noble to send the hosts in at the break 3-0 up. Gary Speed's second half strike makes it a slightly nervous finish, but Hammers go into the final game of the season knowing that the Club's destiny is in their own hands.

13th On a memorable day at Old Trafford against newly-crowned champions Manchester United, a Carlos Tevez strike just before half-time proves to be the only goal of the game, ensuring Premier League football at Upton Park next season. Elsewhere, Wigan's 2-1 victory at Bramall Lane condemns Sheffield United to the Championship, and Fulham's defeat at Middlesbrough means that Alan Curbishley's men eventually finish in 15th place – having been rock bottom and 12 points adrift of safety with just nine games to go!

GOLDEN GOALS

2006-07

Goal 1 - Teddy Sheringham v Blackburn Rovers, Oct 29 2006

How West Ham needed a victory following seven successive defeats! And the wise head of Teddy Sheringham set Hammers on their way to their first win since the opening day of the season. The 40-year-old striker started and finished a superb move that saw him lay the ball wide to Bobby Zamora, who cut-back to Yossi Benayoun. And when the inventive Israeli delivered an inch-perfect cross to the near post, an unmarked Teddy was there to nod the ball beyond Brad Friedel.

Goal 2 - Teddy Sheringham v Portsmouth, Dec 26 2006

Hammers were trailing to two Linvoy Primus headers when former Pompey-striker Teddy Sheringham stepped from the bench to net his 30th and final goal for the Hammers. Anton Ferdinand unsettled the hitherto unflappable Sol Campbell in the area, leaving Teddy to take full advantage of all the confusion and clip an angled consolation beyond the stranded David James towards the far post, where another ex-Hammer Glen Johnson could only help to toe-poke the ball over the line.

Goal 3 - Yossi Benayoun v Fulham, Jan 13 2007

Anyone taking too long over their half-time hot-dog would have missed this Yossi Benayoun barnstormer. The impatient Israeli took just 13 seconds to conjure up a moment of second half brilliance in a game that was destined to finish 3-3. With the crowd still returning to their seats, Bobby Zamora chested the ball into Benayoun's path and he instinctively floated an inch-perfect 18-yarder over the stranded Jan Lastuvka and under the crossbar to give Hammers a 2-1 lead.

Goal 4 - Carlos Tevez v Tottenham Hotspur, March 4 2007

It had been a long time coming. But the wait was well and truly worth it when Carlos Tevez finally netted his first-ever Hammers' goal. Michael Dawson upended the Argentinian ace on the edge of the Spurs' area and after wiping away the mud, Tevez curled a delicious, curling free-kick in off Paul Robinson's crossbar before ripping off his jersey and hurdling into an equally ecstatic crowd at the expense of a booking. Sadly, his joy at giving West Ham a two-goal lead was short-lived for Hammers ended up losing 3-4.

Goal 5 - Bobby Zamora v Arsenal, Apr 7 2007

Hammers, historically, were the last team ever to win at Highbury. And thanks to Bobby Zamora they were also the first side to leave Arsenal's new Emirates Stadium with three points, too. Robert Green had heroically boarded up his goal as the Gunners unsuccessfully tried anything and everything to break the deadlock. But in first-half stoppage time, they were shot down by 'Zamo' who raced onto Lucas Neill's brilliant through-ball and, as Kolo Toure hesitated, the Hammers striker cleverly clipped a 25-yarder over the advancing Jens Lehmann.

Goal 6 - Carlos Tevez v Chelsea, Apr 18 2007

Hammers may have lost 1-4 but at least they had the consolation of scoring the goal of the game. Having just seen his team fall behind, Carlos Tevez's unstoppable response from the left-hand edge of the penalty area whipped around Michael Essien, over the ducking Ricardo Carvalho and through the scorched palms of Petr Cech to fill an ecstatic Upton Park with brief hope.

Goal 7 - Bobby Zamora v Everton, Apr 21 2007

With just four games remaining, Hammers knew that they could not afford to come unstuck against the Toffees. And Bobby Zamora duly found his shooting boots to keep our survival hopes alive with this 13th-minute winner. Yossi Benayoun invited the club's top-scorer to stroll onto his neat back-heel and claim his 11th goal of the season with a curling 20-yarder that sizzled past Alan Stubbs and under the static Tim Howard's right-hand angle.

Goal 8 - Carlos Tevez v Bolton, May 5 2007

Going into the final home game of the season, Hammers fans had, by now, acquired a taste for Carlos Tevez free-kicks. And the South American striker duly left them with the memory of yet another precision strike. This time, it was Abdoulaye Meite who paid the price for a careless lunge on the Argentinian artist. And after dusting himself down, Tevez curled the consequent, inch-perfect, 20-yard free-kick over the Wanderers' wall and under the right-hand angle of the sprawling Jussi Jaaskelainen to send Upton Park wild...again!

Goal 9 - Mark Noble v Bolton Wanderers, May 5 2007

Two-goal Carlos Tevez also turned provider against the Trotters when he floated a delicate cross into no-man's land at the far post. But the Argentinian's extraordinary vision was rewarded with a spectacular coaching manual volley by the in-rushing Mark Noble, who gave the hungry Hammers a stunning three-goal interval lead.

Goal 10 - Carlos Tevez v Manchester United, May 13 2007

Carlos Tevez gatecrashed the Old Trafford Premiership-title party with his seventh strike in 10 games. Robert Green's huge drop-kick was nodded on by Bobby Zamora to his South American strike-partner. Playing a neat one-two with 'Zamo' Tevez raced onto the return and after striding past Wes Brown's weak lunge, he slotted an angled eight-yarder across the face of Edwin Van Der Sar to give Hammers the unlikely, yet priceless, Survival Sunday victory that secured their place in the Premiership.

Statistics 2006-07

Premiership

Date	Opposition	H/A	Score
Sat 19 Aug	Charlton	H	Won 3 - 1
Tue 22 Aug	Watford	A	Drew 1 - 1
Sat 26 Aug	Liverpool	A	Lost 1 - 2
Sun 10 Sep	Aston Villa	H	Drew 1 - 1
Sun 17 Sep	Newcastle	H	Lost 0 - 2
Sat 23 Sep	Man City	A	Lost 0 - 2
Sun 01 Oct	Reading	H	Lost 0 - 1
Sat 14 Oct	Portsmouth	A	Lost 0 - 2
Sun 22 Oct	Tottenham	A	Lost 0 - 1
Sun 29 Oct	Blackburn	H	Won 2 - 1
Sun 05 Nov	Arsenal	H	Won 1 - 0
Sat 11 Nov	Middlesboro	A	Lost 0 - 1
Sat 18 Nov	Chelsea	A	Lost 0 - 1
Sat 25 Nov	Sheff Utd	H	Won 1 - 0
Sun 03 Dec	Everton	A	Lost 0 - 2
Wed 06 Dec	Wigan	H	Lost 0 - 2
Sat 09 Dec	Bolton	A	Lost 0 - 4
Sun 17 Dec	Man Utd	H	Won 1 - 0
Sat 23 Dec	Fulham	A	Drew 0 - 0
Tue 26 Dec	Portsmouth	H	Lost 1 - 2
Sat 30 Dec	Man City	H	Lost 0 - 1
Mon 01 Jan	Reading	A	Lost 0 - 6
Sat 13 Jan	Fulham	H	Drew 3 - 3
Sat 20 Jan	Newcastle	A	Drew 2 - 2
Tue 30 Jan	Liverpool	H	Lost 1 - 2
Sat 03 Feb	Aston Villa	A	Lost 0 - 1
Sat 10 Feb	Watford	H	Lost 0 - 1
Sat 24 Feb	Charlton	A	Lost 0 - 4
Sun 04 Mar	Tottenham	H	Lost 3 - 4
Sat 17 Mar	Blackburn	A	Won 2 - 1
Sat 31 Mar	Middlesboro	H	Won 2 - 0
Sat 07 Apr	Arsenal	A	Won 1 - 0
Sat 14 Apr	Sheff Utd	A	Lost 0 - 3
Wed 18 Apr	Chelsea	H	Lost 1 - 4
Sat 21 Apr	Everton	H	Won 1 - 0
Sat 28 Apr	Wigan	A	Won 3 - 0
Sat 05 Apr	Bolton	H	Won 3 - 1
Sun 13 Apr	Man Utd	A	Won 1 - 0

FA Cup

Date	Round	Opposition	H/A	Score
Sat 06 Jan	Rd 3	Brighton	H	Won 3 - 0
Sat 27 Jan	Rd 4	Watford	H	Lost 0 - 1

Carling Cup

Date	Round	Opposition	H/A	Score
Tue 24 Oct	Rd 2	Chesterfield	A	Lost 1 - 2

UEFA Cup

Date	Round	Opposition	H/A	Score
Thu 14 Sep	Rd 1 1st leg	Palermo	H	Lost 0 - 1
Thu 28 Sep	Rd 1 2nd leg	Palermo	A	Lost 0 - 3

Appearances

Player	Apps	Player	Apps
Benayoun, Yossi	27(2)	Mullins, Hayden	23(7)
Blanco, Kepa	1(7)	Neill, Lucas	12
Boa Morte, Luis	10(6)	Newton, Shaun	1(4)
Bowyer, Lee	18(1)	Noble, Mark	11
Carroll, Roy	14	Pantsil, John	4(2)
Cole, Carlton	7(5)	Quashie, Nigel	8
Collins, James	16	Reid, Kyel	1
Dailly, Christian	13(2)	Reo-Coker, Nigel	37
Davenport, Calum	5(1)	Sheringham, Teddy	4(6)
Etherington, Matthew	23(4)	Spector, Jonathan	18(9)
Ferdinand, Anton	33	Tevez, Carlos	20(3)
Gabbidon, Danny	20	Upson, Matthew	2
Green, Robert	25	Zamora, Bobby	29(5)
Harewood, Marlon	20(6)		
Konchesky, Paul	22		
Mascherano, Javier	3(1)		
McCartney, George	19(3)		
Mears, Tyrone	3(1)		

Final League Table

	Team	P	W	D	L	F	A	GD	PTS
1	Man Utd	38	28	5	5	83	27	56	89
2	Chelsea	38	24	11	3	64	24	40	83
3	Liverpool	38	20	8	10	57	27	30	68
4	Arsenal	38	19	11	8	63	35	28	68
5	Tottenham	38	17	9	12	57	54	3	60
6	Everton	38	15	13	10	52	36	16	58
7	Bolton	38	16	8	14	47	52	-5	56
8	Reading	38	16	7	15	52	47	5	55
9	Portsmouth	38	14	12	12	45	42	3	54
10	Blackburn	38	15	7	16	52	54	-2	52
11	Aston Villa	38	11	17	10	43	41	2	50
12	Middlesbrough	38	12	10	16	44	49	-5	46
13	Newcastle	38	11	10	17	38	47	-9	43
14	Man City	38	11	9	18	29	44	-15	42
15	West Ham	38	12	5	21	35	59	-24	41
16	Fulham	38	8	15	15	38	60	-22	39
17	Wigan	38	10	8	20	37	59	-22	38
18	Sheff Utd	38	10	8	20	32	55	-23	38
19	Charlton	38	8	10	20	34	60	-26	34
20	Watford	38	5	13	20	29	59	-30	28

Goals

Player	Gls	Player	Gls
Benayoun, Yossi	3	Mullins, Hayden	3
Blanco, Kepa	1	Noble, Mark	3
Boa Morte, Luis	1	Reo-Coker, Nigel	1
Cole, Carlton	3	Sheringham, Teddy	2
Ferdinand, Anton	1	Tevez, Carlos	7
Harewood, Marlon	5	Zamora, Bobby	11

Yellow/Red Cards

Player	Yc	Rc	Player	Yc	Rc
Benayoun, Yossi	4	0	Mascherano, Javier	1	0
Boa Morte, Luis	1	0	McCartney, George	4	0
Bowyer, Lee	5	0	Mullins, Hayden	4	0
Davenport, Calum	1	0	Neill, Lucas	3	0
Carroll, Roy	2	0	Noble, Mark	2	0
Cole, Carlton	3	0	Pantsil, John	2	0
Collins, James	4	0	Quashie, Nigel	2	0
Dailly, Christian	1	0	Reo-Coker, Nigel	14	0
Etherington, Matthew	3	0	Sheringham, Teddy	3	0
Ferdinand, Anton	5	0	Spector, Jonathan	5	0
Gabbidon, Danny	1	0	Tevez, Carlos	4	0
Harewood, Marlon	4	0	Zamora, Bobby	5	1
Konchesky, Paul	7	1			

Club Honours and Records

HONOURS

League

Division One Best position: 3rd 1985-86
Division Two Champions (2): 1957-58, 1980-81
Runners-Up (3): 1922-23; 1990-91; 1992-93
Championship Play-off Final Winners: 2005

FA Cup

Winners (3): 1964, 1975, 1980
Runners-up (2): 1923, 2006

Football League Cup:

Runners-up (2): 1966, 1981

Football League War Cup:

Winners (1): 1940

FA Charity Shield

Winners: 1964-65 (shared)

European Competition

European Cup Winners' Cup:
Winners: 1964-65
Runners-Up: 1975-76
UEFA Intertoto Cup:
Winners: 1999

Youth FA Youth Cup

Winners (3): 1963, 1981, 1999
Runners-up(4): 1957, 1959, 1975, 1996
South-East Counties Champions: 1984-85, 1995-96, 1997-98
FA Premier Youth Academy Under-19 Champions: 1998-99,1999-2000

RECORDS

Record Attendance
42,322 v Tottenham Hotspur,
Division One 17/10/70

Record Victories

Division One:
Home: 8-0 v Sunderland, 19/10/68
Away: 6-1 v Manchester City, 8/9/62

Division Two:
Home: 8-0 Rotherham Utd, 8/3/58
Away: 6-0 Leicester City, 15/2/23

FA Cup:
Home: 8-1 v Chesterfield (Rd 1), 10/1/14
Away: 5-0 v Chatham (Rd 5 Q), 28/11/03

League Cup:
Home: 10-0 v Bury (Rd 2 leg 2), 25/10/83
Away: 5-1 v Cardiff City (sf leg 2), 2/2/66 & 5-1 v Walsall (Rd 2), 13/9/67

Europe:
5-1 v Castilla (Rd 1 leg 2) Cup-Winners' Cup, 1/10/80

Record Defeats
League:

Division One:
Home: 2-8 v Blackburn Rovers 26/12/63
Away: 0-7 Everton 22/10/27 & 0-7 v Sheffield Wednesday 28/11/59

Division Two:
Home: 0-6 v Sheffield Wednesday 8/12/51
Away: 0-7 v Barnsley 1/9/19

FA Cup:
Home: 1-5 v Huddersfield Town (Rd 3 rep) 13/1/60
Away: 0-6 v Manchester United (Rd 4) 26/1/03

League Cup:
Home: 2-5 v Barnsley (Rd 2 leg 2) 6/10/87
Away: 0-6 v Oldham Athletic (sf leg 1) 14/2/90

Most League Goals In A Season
101, Division Two 1957-58

Top League Scorer In A Season
Vic Watson (42) Div. One 1929-30

Top Scorer In A Season
Vic Watson (50) Div. One 1929-30

Most Goals In One Match
Vic Watson (6) v Leeds United (h) 9/2/29
Geoff Hurst (6) v Sunderland (h) 19/10/68
Brian Dear (5) v WBA (h) 16/4/65*
*Dear scored all 5 goals in 20 mins either side of half-time which equalled the national record

Most League Goals In Total
Vic Watson (298) 1920-35

Most Goals In Career
Vic Watson (326) 1920-35 (Lge: 298, FA Cup 28)

Most Capped Player
Bobby Moore (England) 108 full caps

Record Transfer Fee Paid
£7.5m to Liverpool for Craig Bellamy, July 2007

Record Transfer Fee Received
£18m from Leeds United for Rio Ferdinand, November 2000

Record Appearances
Billy Bonds 781/12 (1967-88)
(League: 655/8, FA Cup: 46/2, League Cup: 65/2, Europe: 15)

Upton Park

Ground Capacity: 35,146 (All seats)
Pitch Size: 110 x 70 yards
Nearest Tube Station: Upton Park (5 minutes walk)

West Ham United FC

Year Formed:
1895 as Thames Iron Works FC
1900 as West Ham United FC

Turned Professional:
1898 as Thames Iron Works FC

Limited Company: 1900

Former Name:
Thames Iron Works FC (1895-1900)

Club Nicknames:
'Irons' or 'Hammers'

Previous Grounds:
1895-96 Hermit Road Ground
1896-97 Browning Road
1897-1904 Memorial Grounds
1904- Boleyn Ground, Upton Park

Football League & Premiership Record:
Southern League: 1898-1915
Division Two: 1919-23, 1932-58, 1978-81, 1989-91, 1992-93
Division One: 1923-32, 1958-78, 1981-89, 1991-92
Division One (formerly Div. Two): 1992-93, 2003-04
FA Premiership: 1993-03: 2005-
FL Championship (formerly Division One): 2004-05

UPTON PARK

Boleyn Ground, Green Street, Upton Park, London E13 9AZ

Telephone No: 020 8548 2748 Ticket Office: 0870 112 2700

Fax Number: 020 8548 2758 Website: www.whufc.com

2006-07 Quiz

Test your knowledge of last season with our exclusive quick-fire quiz...

1. Who scored West Ham United's first goal of the 2006-07 season?

2. Which team did West Ham United face in the UEFA Cup first round?

3. What was the score in our Carling Cup third round defeat against Chesterfield in October?

4. Who scored the winning goal in our 1-0 home victory against Arsenal in November?

5. Against which team did Alan Curbishley take charge of West Ham United for the first time?

6. Who did West Ham United defeat in the FA Cup third round at Upton Park?

7. Which player signed from Blackburn Rovers in the January transfer window?

8. Who scored West Ham United's goal in our 2-1 home defeat against Liverpool on January 31?

9. How many goals in total were scored during our home match against Tottenham Hotspur in March?

10. Who scored the first goal of the game in our 3-0 win over Wigan Athletic on April 28?

11. Which players scored our goals in the 3-1 win over Bolton Wanderers on May 5?

12. Name the West Ham United starting line-up for our final Premier League match of the season against Manchester United at Old Trafford?

Answers on page 61

Wordsearch

Can you find the surnames of 12 current Hammers stars within the grid?

Answers on page 61

F	R	Y	W	N	B	F	A	K	A	T	E	Y	D	F	C	E	R
G	F	Q	Z	A	M	O	R	A	B	E	L	L	O	M	O	D	O
I	N	E	R	E	E	F	U	O	I	E	R	S	V	U	L	C	M
B	R	O	R	G	R	E	E	N	O	T	S	F	E	A	L	O	A
R	T	I	B	R	L	M	B	G	B	R	C	A	R	B	I	I	S
D	F	I	O	L	O	O	E	G	C	D	O	U	T	B	N	K	N
T	F	G	I	L	E	S	R	E	D	G	R	B	S	I	S	I	I
I	D	H	P	L	M	P	Y	Y	S	G	E	E	O	O	I	L	L
S	Z	L	T	E	Y	U	T	N	E	I	L	L	N	J	G	L	L
D	S	F	A	S	H	T	O	N	S	R	E	L	V	G	D	F	O
E	C	E	W	I	C	D	Z	N	E	Y	Y	A	G	U	I	A	A
G	S	R	S	N	I	N	A	T	T	U	T	M	D	E	I	U	R
J	D	L	C	B	I	O	M	R	Y	D	X	Y	A	R	H	B	F
L	F	L	B	L	L	T	S	U	P	S	O	N	W	O	R	E	B
S	P	A	R	K	E	R	O	A	F	D	S	R	S	A	E	R	R
D	G	O	B	E	I	H	N	C	D	F	S	A	U	I	S	T	T
F	Y	M	G	R	L	S	M	C	C	A	R	T	N	E	Y	D	F
F	A	H	A	E	J	A	A	R	G	D	S	U	Y	I	R	D	A

- ☐ GREEN
- ☐ GABBIDON
- ☐ COLLINS
- ☐ NEILL
- ☐ NOBLE
- ☐ MCCARTNEY
- ☐ ASHTON
- ☐ BELLAMY
- ☐ ZAMORA
- ☐ PARKER
- ☐ FAUBERT
- ☐ UPSON

Pre-season training in Austria.

Dean, you must be delighted just to be playing football again?

"It's brilliant. I know people are going to be analysing everything I do at the moment, but that's not how I'm looking at it. I'm just going out and really enjoying playing football again. Just the simple things like being able to knock a ball around with the lads and getting myself ready for matches – it's a wonderful feeling.

"Obviously there is pressure when a new season starts but I honestly can't see myself feeling too much pressure any more after what I've been through. I put a bit of pressure on myself to do well, but I just really want to enjoy playing football from now on."

Does it worry you that the spotlight is going to be on you as soon as you return?

"No, because any player who has been out for a year is going to have a hawk-eye on him. I know people are going to be looking at my every move, asking: 'Is he alright?' or 'Is he as good as he was?' and all that sort of stuff, but the last thing I need to be worrying about is what others are thinking.

"I know I'm right, I know I'm fine, it's just a case of getting used to the everyday aspects of playing regular football again."

What was the lowest point of your 12 months on the sidelines?

"The lowest point was probably just before I had to have the second operation on the ankle. Until that option was put to me, I was thinking to myself: 'I'm going nowhere, I'm not even getting close, am I ever going to get back?' It was totally soul-destroying. To go out on the pitch and not be able to run properly or kick a ball was very hard to take.

"I saw three specialists and eventually went with a guy called James Calder, who carried out the operation. From then on, it has been totally different. Having not made any progress in the six months before that, suddenly it became a natural progression and I could see the light at the end of the tunnel."

Was there anyone who was particularly supportive during the darkest times?

"My fiancée Gemma was fantastic. She had to put up with me coming home miserable and frustrated, but was always trying to make me feel positive when I was saying that it wasn't right. We have our first baby on the way soon, and that has also put a lot of things in to perspective for me, too.

"The physios who worked with me, Steve Allen and John Green, were also very positive. They kept telling me that I would get back, it was just a case of doing the right thing. And I got to the point where I said to myself that I will do whatever it takes. If it meant working day and night, then I was prepared to do it."

Are you happy with the progress that you have made since returning to action?

"Yes, very happy. I know I've still got things to work on, but I'm not worried about the football side of things – that is just going to be a matter of time.

"If you are out for two weeks, you can come back and be misjudging headers and things like that, so to come back after a year out makes it even harder, but to be involved in the pre-season build-up was just a bonus in itself.

"That's why I was so pleased to get through my first 45 minutes at Dagenham in our opening friendly of the summer. That was only my 10th day of actual football, so it was still very early days for me in terms of the comeback.

"In your head, you think 'yeah, I'll soon be back to where I was previously' but it really isn't that simple. It is going to take me some time to get back to where I was, although that isn't going to stop me progressing.

"Physically, I am better than I was last year – I'm as fit as I have ever been. But you can just run all day – that doesn't recreate a match situation. Playing football is what I need to do now, and it's a great feeling to know that I am back doing what I love."

Has your outlook on the game – and perhaps life in general – changed now?

"Definitely. After this experience, there is nothing in football that could worry me. The whole situation has changed my outlook massively and it has made me appreciate what I've got. I also think it has made me a lot stronger mentally.

"It may sound a bit daft but, when you can't walk, you suddenly realise what life is like for people who have to suffer that permanently. I now appreciate just being able to run freely and kick a ball – and I want to do that for as long as possible."

DEAN ASHTON:

BACK IN BUSINESS!

After almost a year on the sidelines with a broken ankle sustained while on international duty with England, the return to action of striker Dean Ashton was the equivalent of a brand new signing for Hammers boss Alan Curbishley, who finally had the pleasure of naming the 23-year-old in his starting line-up during the 2007-08 pre-season build-up. Now fully fit, Deano is slowly but surely working his way back towards the level of form that originally earned him a place in Steve McClaren's plans, and looking forward to banging in the goals at Upton Park again...

New Signings

Scott Parker, Midfielder
Squad Number: 8
Date signed: 6 June 2007
Signed from: Newcastle United
Fee: £7million
Former Clubs: Charlton, Chelsea, Newcastle United
Honours: PFA Young Player of the Year 2004, Premier League winner 2004-05
International: England - 3 full caps

Richard Wright, Goalkeeper
Squad Number: 21
Date signed: 6 June 2007
Signed from: Everton
Fee: Free
Former Clubs: Ipswich Town, Arsenal, Everton
Honours: Premier League winner 2001-02, FA Cup winner 2002, Division One Play Off winner 2000
International: England - 2 full caps

Julien Faubert, Midfielder

Squad Number: 20
Date signed: 1 July 2007
Signed from: Bordeaux
Fee: £6.1million
Former Clubs: Cannes, Bordeaux
International: France - 1 full cap

Craig Bellamy, Striker

Squad Number: 10
Date signed: 10 July 2007
Signed from: Liverpool
Fee: £7.5million
Former Clubs: Norwich City, Coventry City, Newcastle United, Blackburn Rovers, Celtic (loan), Liverpool
Honours: PFA Young Player of the Year 2002, Scottish FA Cup winner 2005, Community Shield winner 2006
International: Wales - 45 full caps

Freddie Ljungberg, Midfielder

Squad Number: 7
Date signed: 23 July 2007
Signed from: Arsenal
Fee: Undisclosed
Former Clubs: Halmstads BK, Arsenal
Honours: Swedish Cup Winner 1995, Swedish League Winner 1997, Community Shield winner 1999, Premier League Winner 2001-02, 2003-04, FA Cup winner 2002, 2003, 2005
International: Sweden - 67 full caps

Who Am I Quiz

1 WHO AM I?

I was born on October 13, 1980

I grew up in Lambeth, London

I attended the FA School of Excellence as a youngster

In 2004 I won the PFA Young Player of the Year award

I have played at every level from under-15 to senior for England

I made six appearances on loan with Norwich City in 2000

2 WHO AM I?

My middle name is Leon

I began my professional career with West Bromwich Albion

I have won 32 caps for my country

I joined West Ham United in 2005

I enjoying being a DJ in my spare time

I was born in August 1979

3 WHO AM I?

I began my professional career with Bristol Rovers

I scored eight goals in six games on loan with Bath City

I played for England under-21s in the 2002 European Championships

I turned down the opportunity to play for Trinidad and Tobago at the 2006 World Cup finals

I played for junior side Senrab as a schoolboy

My middle name is Lester

Answers on page 61

New Umbro kit

As they bid to rival the Premier League's leading clubs in 2007-08, West Ham United will certainly look the part on the pitch, after signing an exclusive, three-year Technical partnership with UMBRO.

The UK-based company, who are recognised worldwide as manufacturers of the England national team kit, will be the exclusive supplier of the Club's playing and training kit for the next three seasons.

Following the announcement of the deal, West Ham United Chairman Eggert Magnusson said:

"I am delighted to welcome UMBRO to West Ham United as our new Technical partner. We have worked very hard to find the right brand to match our ambition as a football club and believe that UMBRO will provide the perfect solution for all of our technical requirements.

"The deal is an exclusive agreement which means that only West Ham United club stores and whufc.com will stock the Club's official UMBRO merchandise.

"Like West Ham United, UMBRO has a rich heritage and history in the game but is also committed to an exciting and innovative future, and we look forward to a long and successful partnership between the two parties here at Upton Park."

The brand new home kit was launched on June 16, with the away kit released on July 26. Record sales have already been reported in both our Stadium and Lakeside Club Stores, with Hammers fans queuing up to get their hands on the new designs.

Away Kit GoalKeeper

Home Kit GoalKeeper

Away Kit

Home Kit

Spot the difference

Can you spot the SIX differences between the two pictures involving West Ham United players? Answers on page 61

Player Profiles...

Popular goalkeeper who became a legend during his 11 years with Walsall after joining them on a free transfer from the trainee ranks at Notts County in August 1993.

Given his first opportunity in League football by then Walsall manager Kenny Hibbitt, in August 1993, Jimmy made 31 consecutive League appearances for the Saddlers in his first season in senior football, the prelude to a career that saw him become the consistent rock at the back during 447 appearances for the Midlands club.

A free agent in the summer of 2004, Jimmy signed for West Ham United and eventually established himself as first choice at the beginning of April 2005, starting in the final 11 games of the season which climaxed at the Millennium Stadium with the Championship Play-Off Final victory against Preston North End.

Sadly, success came at a price. Coming out for a high ball in the 87th minute, Jimmy over-ran the 18 yard-line and, in trying to check back with the ball in his hands above his head he landed awkwardly, suffering knee ligament damage that ruled him out for the majority of the 2005-06 campaign. Has since battled back to become a valuable member of the Hammers squad.

England international goalkeeper signed from Norwich City on the eve of the 2006-07 campaign in a deal that could eventually rise to £2million.

After making his first-team debut for the Canaries in a 0-0 derby draw with Ipswich Town as a 19-year-old in April 1999, the Chertsey-born keeper went on to make almost 250 league and cup appearances for the club.

He was an influential figure as Norwich won promotion to the Premiership in 2004, and was rewarded for his performances in the top flight with a call-up to the full England squad - becoming only the sixth Norwich player in history to wear the Three Lions when he appeared as a substitute against Colombia in the United States in June 2005.

He was set to travel to the World Cup finals in Germany last summer as a possible number two behind Paul Robinson However, disaster struck when Robert suffered a serious groin injury minutes after appearing as a substitute in a B international against Belarus at the end of May, ruling him out of the tournament.

After a summer of rehabilitation, he earned a move back to the Premiership with the Hammers, and became a key figure in our successful fight against relegation, particularly with his memorable display in the 1-0 win over Arsenal at the Emirates Stadium in April.

Jimmy Walker, Goalkeeper
Born: Sutton-in-Ashfield, 9 July 1973
Signed from: Walsall

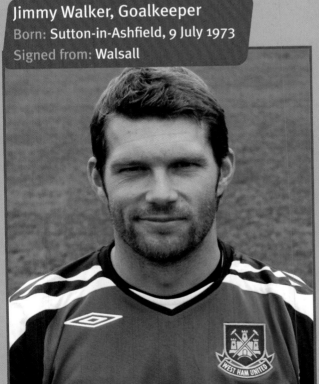

Robert Green, Goalkeeper
Born: Chertsey, 18 January 1980
Signed from: Norwich City

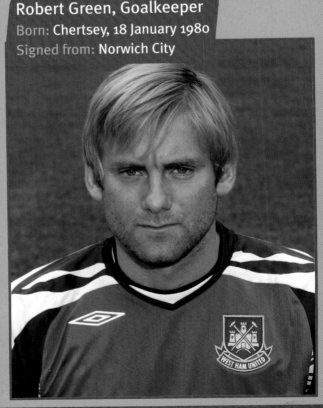

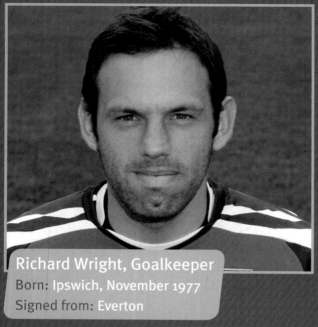

Richard Wright, Goalkeeper
Born: Ipswich, November 1977
Signed from: Everton

England international goalkeeper signed on a Bosman free transfer in the summer of 2007. The 29-year-old former Ipswich Town, Arsenal and Everton stopper was a free agent after leaving Goodison Park at the end of last season.

Born in Ipswich in November 1977, Richard joined his hometown club as a schoolboy and progressed to make his first team debut in the old First Division at the age of just 18, in a 1-0 defeat at Manchester City in August 1996.

After establishing himself as a regular in the team almost immediately, the young keeper went on to suffer defeat in three successive play-off semi-finals before making it fourth time lucky in May 2000 - saving a penalty as Ipswich beat Barnsley at Wembley to reach the Premier League.

Just five days after his promotion triumph, Richard made his full international debut for England in a 2-1 friendly win over Malta - saving another penalty to further enhance his growing reputation as one of the country's most promising young goalkeepers and earn him a place in the Euro 2000 finals squad.

After one more season at Portman Road - in which he helped lead the newly-promoted Tractor Boys to a top five finish and UEFA Cup qualification - Richard earned a £6million move to Arsenal in the summer of 2001 and went on to make 22 league and cup appearances in the 2001-02 season, including four in the Champions League, winning a Premiership winners' medal.

However, after just a solitary season in north London, the 6ft 2ins stopper was on the move again, this time in a £3.5million switch to Everton. Sadly, knee and ankle injuries blighted much of his career on Merseyside, and the arrival of Tim Howard on loan from Manchester United last season restricted him to just two appearances in his final campaign at Goodison.

Lucas Neill, Defender
Born: Sydney, Australia, 9 March 1978
Signed from: Blackburn Rovers

Australian national team captain who joined West Ham United from Blackburn Rovers for an undisclosed fee in January 2007. The 29-year-old endured a nightmare start to his Upton Park career, suffering an ankle injury on his debut against Watford, but battled back to become a major influence as Alan Curbishley's men avoided relegation with seven wins in the last nine matches.

Born in Sydney, Australia in March 1978, Lucas was registered on a football scholarship with the Australian Institute of Sport after leaving college in 1994, before moving to London at the age of 17 in November 1995 to join Millwall. He spent six years at The Den, before signing for Blackburn in a £1million deal in 2001.

A reliable and versatile performer who, although recognised as a right-back, is comfortable in the centre of defence, Lucas made 227 league and cup appearances for Rovers, enjoying two UEFA Cup campaigns and missing just a handful of matches throughout his career with the club.

Currently captain of the Australian national team, Lucas made his full international debut at the age of just 18, against Saudi Arabia in October 1996, and has since gone on to win 29 caps for his country, becoming the 50th player to captain Australia when he was handed the armband last October.

Highly-rated young defender who has progressed through the ranks to become another major success story of the West Ham United Youth Academy system.

Like all youngsters thrown into the senior fray, Anton experienced mixed fortunes in his first season of League football after making his debut at Preston in the opening fixture of the 2003-04 season; a campaign in which he featured across the back-line but predominantly at right-back.

Anton made his England Under-21 bow against the Ukraine in August 2004 and celebrated his 50th senior League appearance against Ipswich Town in the home-leg of the Play-Off semi-final of May 2005. Good in the air and calm under pressure, he reads the game well and, while he may be the younger brother of former Hammer Rio, he is now established as a star in his own right.

Anton signed a new four-year contract just before the start of the 2005-06 season and impressed so much he was rewarded with a brand new deal in January 2006. Suffered a number of niggling injuries during the 2006-07 campaign, ruling him out of action for varying spells, but returned to the heart of the defence for the run-in, and then travelled to Holland with England for the European Under-21 Championships in the summer.

Scottish international defender who is currently the club's longest-serving player, and has experienced promotion, relegation, an FA Cup final, two play-off finals, and serious injury during his six years at Upton Park.

A former trainee with Dundee United, he made 143 Scottish League appearances scoring 18 goals in his six years at Tannadice Park. While at United, he won a record 34 Scotland Under-21 caps. Christian cost Derby County £1million when they signed him in August 1996 after a move to the continent had broken down.

His sterling performances prompted Craig Brown to give him his first full cap against Wales in May 1997 and a week later he scored his first international goal against Malta. Following the World Cup finals in 1998, Blackburn Rovers invested £5.3 million to secure his services and Christian made 70 Premiership appearances before transferring to the Hammers in January 2001.

Strong in the air, decisive in his tackling, and possessing pace and positional instinct, Christian proved to be an influential leader after his appointment as captain for the 2003-04 season. Despite having to sit out much of our last two Premiership campaigns, he has been an influential figure in the dressing-room and given 100% whenever called upon.

Anton Ferdinand, Defender
Born: Peckham, 18 February 1985
Signed from: Trainee

Christian Dailly, Defender
Born: Dundee, 23 October 1973
Signed from: Blackburn Rovers

Danny Gabbidon, Defender
Born: Cwmbran, Wales, 8 August 1979
Signed from: Cardiff City

James Collins, Defender
Born: Newport, 23 August 1983
Signed from: Cardiff City

Joined Hammers in the summer of 2005 from Cardiff City. Began his career with West Bromwich Albion and made two league appearances for the Baggies but moved to Ninian Park for £175,000 in August 2000 and quickly established himself as a key figure in the Bluebirds defence.

Won his first cap for Wales against the Czech Republic in March 2002 and was selected in the PFA's First Division team of the season in 2003-04. Danny continued to flourish at club and international levels, showing great awareness and a composure on the ball that had him earmarked for a higher grade of football.

That chance came when Alan Pardew pounced to secure his services in the summer of 2005, and the cultured defender was one of the outstanding success stories of our first season back in the Premiership. Sadly, injury limited his chances in the 2006-07 campaign and he made only a couple of appearances under Alan Curbishley, but is now back to full fitness.

James was just 17 when he was introduced into the Cardiff City first-team in November 2000 in an FA Cup First Round tie against Bristol Rovers

This was the first of 85 senior games he would play for the Ninian Park club before his departure to East London on the same day as his central defensive partner Danny Gabbidon in the summer of 2005.

He saw his move to Upton Park as a positive chance to enhance his international future as well, after enjoying his baptism for Wales against Norway in May 2004; inscribing his name into the history books as the first Welsh player to hold caps at every level for his country.

He was forced to start the 2005-06 on the sidelines following the superb form of Gabbidon and Anton Ferdinand at the back, but he took his chance when injury struck his fellow countryman and he has made several impressive appearances since his introduction to the Premier League, including some rock-solid displays at the end of last season, as Hammers avoided relegation.

Northern Ireland international defender signed from Sunderland in a deal worth £1million in August 2006.

Hammers paid the Black Cats £600,000 and added Clive Clarke to the package to secure the services of the 25-year-old left-back, who progressed through the youth ranks at the Stadium of Light to become club captain.

Born in Belfast, George has 19 international caps to his name. He made his senior debut for Northern Ireland in September 2001 in a World Cup qualifying match against Iceland, scoring the final goal in a 3-0 victory – the only strike of his professional career so far.

He left Sunderland having made almost 150 league and cup appearances for the Club and made his Hammers debut in the Carling Cup defeat at Chesterfield in October 2006.

George McCartney, Defender
Born: Belfast, 29 April 1981
Signed from: Sunderland

Talented central defender who joined the select band of players to have enjoyed two spells at Upton Park when he signed from Tottenham Hotspur for an undisclosed fee in January 2007.

Born in Bedford on New Year's Day 1983, the former England youth and under-21 international began his professional career with Coventry City, before earning a move to the Premiership in August 2004, when Tottenham swooped to secure his signature in a £1.5million deal. However, just days later, the 6ft 3ins defender was heading back to the Championship after Spurs agreed to loan their new signing out to West Ham United.

Calum made his Hammers debut in a 2-1 win at Sheffield United and went on to make 10 league appearances for the Club. After impressing in the centre of defence during our push for promotion, it was something of a disappointment when he was recalled by Spurs in mid-November.

After making his long-awaited debut for Tottenham in a 1-0 defeat at Aston Villa, Calum then headed out for further loan spells at Southampton and then at Norwich City the following season, before returning to White Hart Lane to play in their last four matches of the 2005-06 campaign - including their infamous final-day 2-1 defeat at Upton Park.

After winning a place in Martin Jol's team at the start of last season, Calum then found himself on the sidelines as Ledley King and Michael Dawson formed a first-choice partnership and, when Alan Curbishley pounced in January, he had no hesitation in returning to Upton Park.

Calum Davenport, Defender
Born: Bedford, 1 January 1983
Signed from: Tottenham Hotspur

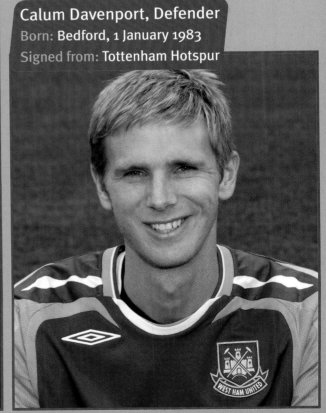

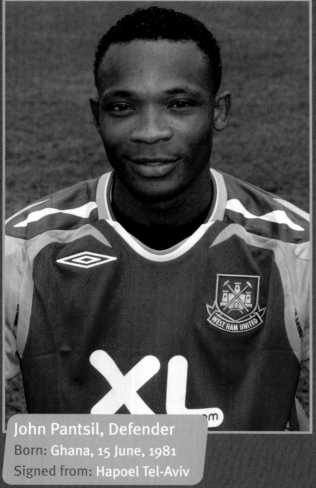

John Pantsil, Defender
Born: Ghana, 15 June, 1981
Signed from: Hapoel Tel-Aviv

Jonathan Spector, Defender
Born: Arlington Heights, USA, 1 March 1986
Signed from: Manchester United

Ghanaian international signed from Israeli side Hapoel Tel-Aviv in the summer of 2006 in a deal that could rise to £1million.

A versatile defender who starred for Ghana at the World Cup finals in Germany this summer, John is recognised as a right-back but has also featured in central defence and at left back for his country.

He began his career in Ghana at Berekum Arsenal FC before moving to Liberty Professionals. He then headed to Europe for a brief spell with Polish side Widzew Lodz, before joining Israeli club Maccabi Tel Aviv in 2002, where he won the Israeli title and reached the Israeli Cup final in his first season. In December 2004, he signed permanently for Hapoel Tel Aviv after completing a short loan move across town from Maccabi.

A member of the Ghana under-21 side that reached the FIFA World Youth Championship final in Argentina in 2001, John soon moved onto senior duty and was selected to play in the 2002 and 2006 African Cup of Nations in Mali & Egypt respectively.

He was also selected for the 2004 Olympic Games in Greece and played all matches at the World Cup finals last summer, when Ghana progressed through the group stages only to be beaten in the second round by Brazil.

USA international defender who joined the Hammers in a £500,000 move from Manchester United in June 2006.

Born and raised in Arlington Heights, a suburb of Chicago, Jonathan moved to England at the age of 17 to join Manchester United in the summer of 2003 and made his senior debut just a year later, in the Community Shield against Arsenal at the Millennium Stadium.

In November 2004, he made his full international debut for the USA, as a substitute in a World Cup qualifying clash against Jamaica. He had to wait almost a year for his second taste of senior international football, in a 2-0 qualifying victory over Panama in October 2005.

By that time, Jonathan had departed from Old Trafford in a bid to find regular first team football - signing for Charlton Athletic on a season-long loan spell at the start of the 2005-06 campaign.

Having impressed Alan Curbishley, Jonathan began to establish himself as a regular in the Addicks side at the turn of 2006 and went on to make 20 Premiership appearances for our London rivals, before securing a permanent move to Upton Park.

A versatile defender, who can play in a number of positions along the back-line, Jonathan is the second USA international to sign for West Ham United - after midfielder John Harkes, who made 13 appearances here in the 1995-96 season.

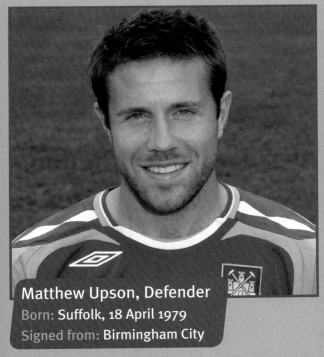

Matthew Upson, Defender
Born: Suffolk, 18 April 1979
Signed from: Birmingham City

Highly-rated central defender signed from Birmingham City for an initial fee of £6million on deadline day in the January transfer window this year.

In a deal that could rise to £7.5million depending on appearances, the 27-year-old England international agreed a four-and-a-half year contract at Upton Park.

Born in Suffolk in April 1979, Matthew was spotted by Luton Town as a youngster and joined the Hatters as a trainee, but made just one senior league appearance for the club - as a 17-year-old against Rotherham United in August 1996 - before Arsenal paid £2million the following year to acquire his services.

After waiting patiently for his big chance under Arsene Wenger, the 6ft 1in central defender won a Premiership title medal in 2001-02, but continued to find first-team opportunities limited at Highbury, and headed out for loan spells with Nottingham Forest, Crystal Palace and Reading, before Birmingham City paid £1million to make him a permanent signing in January 2003.

The former England under-21 international played a key role as Blues retained their newly-acquired Premiership status at the end of the campaign, and he was then rewarded with a call-up to the full national team, making his debut in a friendly against South Africa in Durban on May 22, 2003.

He went on to win seven full caps under Sven-Goran Eriksson, the last of which came in a 1-0 friendly defeat against Spain at the Bernabeu stadium in November 2004, and has been a key performer for Birmingham City during the past four years, making almost 130 league and cup appearances. Sadly, his Hammers debut ended in disappointment, as a calf injury forced him off after just 28 minutes of our 1-0 defeat at Aston Villa, and an aborted comeback against Tottenham a month later forced him to miss the rest of the campaign.

Scott Parker, Midfielder
Born: Lambeth, 13 October 1980
Signed from: Newcastle United

England international midfielder signed from Newcastle United in a £7million deal this summer. Born and raised in Lambeth, South London the 26-year-old has represented England at every level from Under-15s to senior.

He signed for Alan Curbishley's Charlton Athletic as a trainee and made his senior debut against Bury in August 1997. He enjoyed a brief loan spell with Norwich City in 2000 to gain more experience and returned to the Valley, immediately establishing himself as an assured first team player. He made 145 appearances for the Addicks, scoring 10 times.

Scott's skills soon caught the eye of then-England manager Sven-Goran Eriksson and he was given his international debut in January 2003 against Denmark, when he came on as a substitute. He joined Chelsea for £10m a year later, in January 2004, and was named PFA Young Player of the Year at the end of the 2003-04 season.

He joined Newcastle United for £6.5 million at the start of the 2005-06 campaign and was awarded the captaincy on the eve of the 2006-07 season. He became Alan Curbishley's first summer signing this year when he signed a £7million five-year deal with the Hammers on June 6, 2007.

Luis Boa Morte, Midfielder
Born: Lisbon, Portugal, 4 August 1977
Signed from: Fulham

Portuguese international winger who became Alan Curbishley's first signing as West Ham United manager when he moved from Fulham for an undisclosed fee in January 2007.

Born in Lisbon in August 1977, Luis began his professional career with his hometown club, Sporting Lisbon, in 1996, but spent just one season there before moving to England at the age of 19 to join the Gunners in June 1997 for a fee of 1.75million.

In two seasons at Highbury, he made 40 league and cup appearances under Arsene Wenger but, after growing frustrated at his lack of first-team opportunities, was allowed to join Southampton in a £500,000 deal in August 1999.

After spending just one season with the Saints, he moved to Fulham in a season-long loan deal in the summer of 2000 and helped the Londoners win the old First Division Championship in May 2001, scoring the goal against Huddersfield that clinched promotion to the Premiership, before completing a permanent £1.7million transfer to Craven Cottage that summer.

In the same year he won a call-up to Portugal's national team, making his international debut in a 4-0 defeat against France, and has since gone on to win 25 caps for his country, scoring two goals. He was a member of the Portuguese squad that reached the semi-finals of the World Cup in Germany last summer, appearing as a substitute in a 2-1 Group D victory over Mexico.

Hayden Mullins, Midfielder
Born: Reading, 27 March 1979
Signed from: Crystal Palace

Reliable midfielder signed in October 2003 from Crystal Palace, where he had graduated from the trainee ranks to secure his first full contract in February 1997.

Had to wait until August 1998 to get his chance in the first-team at Selhurst Park, which he took with both feet, scoring five times in 40 League appearances in his inaugural season.

A versatile and flexible performer, both Palace and West Ham have utilised his considerable talents to the full and he has filled almost every outfield position. Deployed at centre-half, at right and left-back, as well as wing-back and wide midfield, the former England Under-21 international has been a valued member of the squad thoughout his four years at the Club.

Having proved his versatility in several different positions, Hayden settled into his favoured midfield role in the second half of the 2004-05 season as Hammers headed towards promotion glory, and he has developed into one of our most consistent performers in the Premier League over the past two seasons, attracting much praise for his tidy, no-nonsense displays in the centre of the park.

A natural, good old-fashioned left-winger signed from Tottenham Hotspur in August 2003. Graduated through the junior ranks with Peterborough United and made his League debut for the Posh when only 15 years and 262 days old, when he was in the starting line in a 3-1 defeat at Torquay on April 25, 1998.

Having represented England at Under-16, Under-18 and Under-20 levels, Matthew had a week on trial with Manchester United in the 1999 close-season. On returning to Peterborough he signed a five-year contract, but soon completed a £500,000 move to Tottenham Hotspur in January 2000.

Ironically, his only start for Spurs that season was against Manchester United at Old Trafford and, although acknowledged as an exciting prospect, Matthew was limited to just 20 starts in 45 Premiership outings for the North London club. In October 2001, he went on loan to Bradford City, for whom he made 13 League appearances.

When Matty arrived at Upton Park in part-exchange for Fredi Kanoute in August 2003, he became an instant hit with the home fans, establishing himself as one of the most influential players in the side. He crowned a magnificent first season by winning the Hammer of the Year award.

His pace, tight control, and positive runs deep into opposition territory provide tremendous entertainment and he has stepped up to become a regular and consistent performer in the Premier League.

Swedish international captain signed from Arsenal in July 2007 for an undisclosed fee.

Born in Vittsjo in April 1977, Freddie joined Halmstads in Sweden at the age of five, and played several other sports including ice hockey and handball, for which he was called up to the national squad. He made his senior debut for Halmstads on 23 October 1994 in the Swedish First Division against AIK.

He went on to make 139 appearances and score 16 goals for the club, before earning a £3million move to Arsenal in 1998, when he enjoyed a memorable debut, scoring against Manchester United after coming on as a late substitute.

The 30-year-old midfielder spent nine years with the Gunners, where he made a total of 216 league and cup appearances - including a Champions League Final against Barcelona in May 2006. During his time under Arsene Wenger, he won the Premier League title in 2002 and 2004, and the FA Cup in 2002, 2003 and 2005.

He won his first full cap for Sweden on 24 January 1998 against the USA, and has represented his country at Euro 2000, World Cup 2002, Euro 2004 and World Cup 2006, where his 13th goal for Sweden came in the 89th minute of the match against Paraguay. Appointed captain of the Swedish national team in August 2006, he has won 67 senior caps and scored 13 goals for his country.

Matthew Etherington, Midfielder
Born: Truro, 14 August 1981
Signed from: Tottenham Hotspur

Freddie Ljungberg, Midfielder
Born: Vittsjo, Sweden, 16 April 1977
Signed from: Arsenal

Lee Bowyer, Midfielder
Born: Poplar, London, 3 January 1977
Signed from: Newcastle United

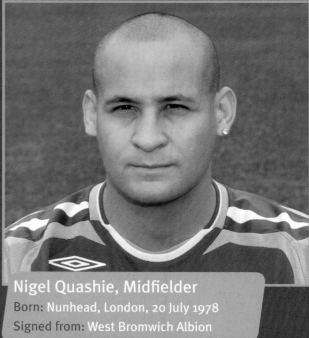

Nigel Quashie, Midfielder
Born: Nunhead, London, 20 July 1978
Signed from: West Bromwich Albion

Former England international midfielder who became a West Ham United player for the second time when he arrived from Newcastle United in June 2006.

Lee made 11 appearances for the Club after joining in a cut-price deal from Leeds United in January 2003, but was unable to help us avoid relegation from the Premiership at the end of that season.

He then joined Newcastle on a Bosman free transfer and went on to score six times in 79 Premier League outings for the Magpies, before his return to London last summer.

Born in Poplar, east London in January 1977, Lee grew up as a Hammers fan and names Billy Bonds as his all-time favourite player. However, after impressing for famous local Sunday side Senrab, he was snapped up as a schoolboy by Charlton Athletic, where he made impressive progress at youth level and went on to make more than 50 senior appearances for the Addicks.

In July 1996, Leeds United swooped with a bid of £2.8million to make 19-year-old Bowyer the most expensive teenager in English football and he repaid that by going on to make more than 250 appearances and score more than 50 goals at Elland Road.

Experienced Scottish international midfielder who completed a £1.5million move from West Bromwich Albion in January 2007.

The transfer signalled a return to his London roots for the 28-year-old. Born in Nunhead, near Peckham, in July 1978, he started his career with Queens Park Rangers and made his professional debut against Manchester United at Old Trafford at the tender age of 17 in December 1995.

After several impressive performances for Rangers, Nigel earned a call-up to the England under-21 squad, before making a £2.5million move to Nottingham Forest in the summer of 1998. However, his first season at the City Ground ended in relegation from the Premiership and, after failing to win promotion back to the top flight the following year, he joined Portsmouth for £600,000 in the summer of 2000.

After establishing himself at Fratton Park and playing a key role in Pompey's First Division Championship triumph in 2003 and subsequent success in retaining their newly-acquired Premiership status, Nigel took advantage of a new FIFA ruling, enabling him to accept the opportunity of full international recognition with Scotland, despite wearing the Three Lions of England as an under-21 player. He made his full debut against Estonia in May 2004.

In January 2005, Nigel was snapped up by his former Pompey manager Harry Redknapp – by now at South Coast rivals Southampton – for a fee of £2.1million, but spent just 12 months at St Mary's before making a £1.2million move to West Bromwich Albion.

Made just seven appearances for the Hammers last season before a nasty foot injury sustained against Tottenham in March ended his campaign.

French international midfielder signed in the summer of 2007 from Bordeaux for a fee of nine million euros (£6.1m).

Born in Le Havre on August 1, 1983, Julien headed south in 1998 when he was offered a place at the AS Cannes youth academy, famous for nurturing such talents as Zinédine Zidane, Johan Micoud and Patrick Vieira. He went on to make 45 senior appearances for the club before moving to Bordeaux in the summer of 2004.

The fast and powerful midfielder earned a call-up to the French national squad following last year's World Cup finals, making his international debut against Bosnia on August 16, when he scored the winning goal in a 2-1 victory.

Julien became one of the hottest properties in French football last season, and the Hammers beat off interest from AS Roma and Rangers to secure his services. However, the Frenchman endured a nightmare start to his career in England, sustaining a ruptured Achilles tendon during the Club's pre-season tour to Austria, an injury that is set to rule him out until early 2008.

Julien Faubert, Midfielder
Born: Le Havre, France, 1 August 1983
Signed from: Bordeaux

A fantastic young talent with a great future in front of him, Mark made his breakthrough into the first-team at the age of 17 and immediately won the hearts of the West Ham fans with his spirited all action style.

A local lad, he joined the Club as a schoolboy and, at the age of 15, became the youngest player ever to appear in the Hammers' reserve team.

A cultured passer of the ball and fearless in the challenge, Mark was first involved with the first team squad during the 2003-04 season and Alan Pardew let him off the leash in August 2004, when he made his senior bow from the subs' bench in our 2-0 home victory over Southend United in the Carling Cup.

He signed a new four-year contract during the summer of 2005, and made his Premiership debut as a substitute on the opening day of the season against Blackburn Rovers, before heading out on loan to Hull City at the end of the season.

He started the 2006-07 campaign on loan, too, at Ipswich Town, but was given his chance by Alan Curbishley in the FA Cup third round tie against Brighton and Hove Albion in January, and responded with his first senior goal for the Club.

He then waited patiently for two months before his next opportunity, and took it in style with another goal and superb all-round performance in the thrilling 4-3 defeat against Spurs. That secured his place in the team, and he went on to play a key role in the final nine games as Hammers pulled off the great escape, before celebrating the achievement with a call-up to the England under-21 squad for the European Championships in Holland, where he made a big impression on coach Stuart Pearce.

Mark Noble, Midfielder
Born: Newham, 8 May 1987
Signed from: Trainee

Bobby Zamora, Forward
Born: Barking, 16 January 1981
Signed from: Tottenham Hotspur

Carlton Cole, Forward
Born: Surrey, 12 November 1983
Signed from: Chelsea

Highly-rated former England under-21 striker, who signed for an undisclosed fee from Chelsea in July 2006.

Highly-rated former England under-21 striker, who signed for an undisclosed fee from Chelsea in July 2006.

Bobby became a Hammers hero when he scored the Play-Off Final goal that took the Club back to the Premiership after a two year exile in May 2005.

Originally began his career with Bristol Rovers, before making his name with Brighton and Hove Albion, where he hit 70 goals in 119 League games.

On the strength of that, Tottenham Hotspur paid £1.5 million for his signature in July 2003, but Bobby was given only six Premiership starts by the North London club and the chance to join West Ham United in an exchange deal involving Jermain Defoe in January 2004 was a dream come true.

An ardent lifelong Hammers fan, Bobby made a scoring debut at Bradford City. However, early on he struggled to make the impact he desired. However, he burst into form in the Play-Off semi-final matches of 2005, blasting Ipswich Town out of the competition with three goals in a 4-2 aggregate victory.

Despite starting the 2005-06 Premiership campaign as third-choice behind Marlon Harewood and Teddy Sheringham, he responded in admirable fashion, taking his chance whenever it appeared and soon fired his way into the starting line-up. Finished as the club's leading goalscorer last season, hitting 11 goals in 37 league and cup appearances.

A product of the youth academy system at Stamford Bridge, 23-year-old Carlton made his first team debut for our London rivals as an 18-year-old substitute against Everton in April 2002.

The following season, he enjoyed a brief loan spell at Wolves, before heading out on loan again at the start of the 2003-04 campaign, to Charlton Athletic on a season-long deal. After five goals in 22 appearances for Alan Curbishley's men, he was forced to head for pastures new again in search of regular first team football.

This time, it was Aston Villa who snapped up the promising young striker on a 12-month loan spell, during which time Jose Mourinho saw enough to declare that Cole would be staying put at Stamford Bridge for the 2005-06 campaign.

However, with Didier Drogba and Hernan Crespo scoring regularly, Carlton again found his chances restricted. After finally cut his ties with Stamford Bridge permanently last summer, Carlton hit a debut goal on the opening day of the season against Charlton Athletic, and went on to make 20 league and cup appearances, scoring two more times.

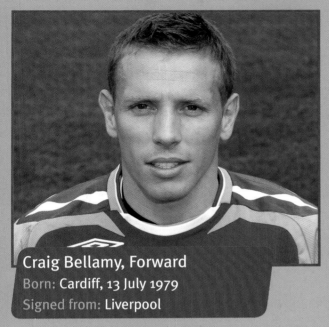

Craig Bellamy, Forward
Born: Cardiff, 13 July 1979
Signed from: Liverpool

Welsh international captain signed from Liverpool in a club record £7.5million deal in the summer of 2007.

Born in Cardiff on July 13, 1979, Craig left home as a teenager to begin his career with Norwich City, where he made his debut against Crystal Palace in March 1997, before going on to net 32 goals in 84 league and cup appearances for the Canaries.

In the summer of 2000, he earned a £6.5million move to Coventry City but, after suffering relegation in his first season at Highfield Road, was again the target of Premier League clubs and, in June 2001, Newcastle United manager Bobby Robson swooped to sign him for £6million.

The Welshman enjoyed a fantastic start to his career at St James' Park, winning the PFA Young Player of the Year award at the end of his first campaign. Following the arrival of Graeme Souness as manager in August 2004, Craig's Newcastle career hit a rocky patch and, in January 2005, he joined Celtic on loan, scoring seven goals in just 12 appearances.

In July 2005, his former national team coach Mark Hughes paid £5million to take Bellamy to Blackburn Rovers, where he again proved his Premier League quality, scoring 13 goals in 27 appearances at Ewood Park, a strike-rate that alerted Liverpool to splash out £6million for his services last summer.

He managed nine goals in 27 appearances for the Reds, including a vital Champions League strike against Barcelona at the Nou Camp that helped Rafael Benitez's men on their way to eventually reaching the final against AC Milan in May, when he was an unused substitute as the Italians sealed a 2-0 victory.

Craig made his senior international debut for Wales against Jamaica at the age of just 18, and has so far earned 45 caps for his country, scoring 13 goals. At the end of last season, following the retirement of Ryan Giggs from international football, the striker was confirmed as the country's new team captain.

A powerful, hugely-talented striker who joined West Ham United Football Club from Norwich City in January 2006 in a £7million deal.

Dean joined Crewe Alexandra as a youngster and, under the watchful eye of Dario Gradi, progressed through the ranks to make his introduction into League football in the 2000-01 season, scoring eight goals in 21 Division One appearances.

Having previously played for England at Under-19 level, he stepped up to the Under-21 side in 2004, scoring against Holland and Sweden, before leaving Gresty Road on January 11 2005, to become Norwich City's record signing at £3million.

Thrust straight into the Premier League, he made his Canaries debut in a 3-0 defeat at Villa Park and, in his 16 Premiership games with Norwich, he finished as the Canaries' joint top scorer with seven goals despite the club's relegation.

In the 2005-06 campaign his progress was interrupted by a sickening fractured forehead, but he was back in action at Christmas, before Hammers swooped to make him a club record signing the following month.

He got off to a fantastic start at Upton Park, scoring on his debut in a 2-0 win over Sunderland, before going on to play a key role in our run to the FA Cup final, where he scored in the 3-3 draw with Liverpool after recovering from a hamstring injury.

An intense fitness programme in the summer of 2006 had him in fantastic shape and he earned his first call-up to the senior England squad a week before the start of the new season. However, disaster struck when he sustained a broken ankle during training with Steve McClaren's men, an injury that ruled him out for the entire 2006-07 campaign.

Now back to full fitness again, Dean began the 2007-08 campaign hoping that he could soon re-discover the form that had made him one of the most exciting young strikers in the country.

Dean Ashton, Forward
Born: Crewe, 24 November 1983
Signed from: Norwich City

YOUNG HAMMERS

We focus on the young players progressing through the Youth Academy ranks who will be hoping to make a first-team breakthrough at Upton Park in the near future...

KYEL REID

A talented left-winger who signed professional forms at Upton Park shortly after his 17th birthday. Kyel joined the Club as an Academy scholar in July 2004 and has risen rapidly through the ranks.

He made his senior debut for the Hammers in a 1-0 victory over West Bromwich Albion at the end of the 2005-06 season, and also appeared in our 2-1 win against Spurs the following week.

Headed out on loan last season to Barnsley, where he made an impressive contribution, and was included in Alan Curbishley's plans during the 2007-08 pre-season build-up.

HOGAN EPHRAIM

Highly-rated young striker who has been tipped for big things at the Club. A regular at various junior England levels, Hogan established himself as a key member of the Under-18 national team last season.

Along with Tony Stokes, he made his senior debut as a substitute in the Carling Cup win at Sheffield Wednesday in September 2005 and has since been making an impact in the reserve team.

Spent a valuable loan spell at Colchester United last season, and will be hoping that he can force his way into Alan Curbishley's plans in the near future.

JACK COLLISON

Stylish midfielder who has made excellent progress in the past 12 months.

Originally joined the Hammers from Cambridge United, where he grew up before the club's demotion from the Football League led to administration and forced him to search for pastures new.

Cambridge's loss was certainly Hammers' gain, for the tall, athletic midfielder has been a key performer for Tony Carr's under-18 squad. Having progressed to the reserve team last season, Jack travelled to Austria on the first-team pre-season tour this summer and is certainly one to keep an eye on in future.

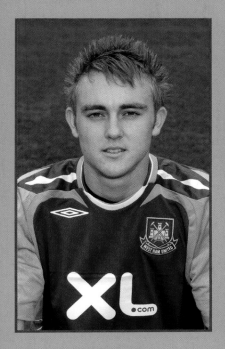

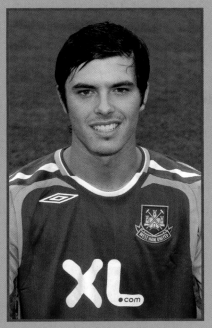

TONY STOKES

Another highly-talented midfield player, who was handed a first-team debut in September 2005 as a substitute in a Carling Cup second round victory over Sheffield Wednesday.

Since then, Tony has been a regular fixture in the reserve team, and has also enjoyed two spells out on loan to gain senior Football League experience. He spent the second half of the 2005-06 campaign with League Two side Rushden and Diamonds, making 19 appearances, then started the 2006-07 season with Brighton and Hove Albion, where he appeared six times before returning to Upton Park.

A troublesome shoulder injury restricted his progress for the rest of the campaign, but Tony still made a handful of reserve team appearances and was also involved with the first-team pre-season build-up this summer.

JAMES TOMKINS

Hugely-talented central defender who has represented England at every level from schoolboy to under-18, and was on the verge of breaking through to the Hammers first team squad at the start of last season before a dislocated shoulder disrupted his progress.

The Basildon-born youngster had appeared in several pre-season friendlies before the 2006-07 campaign, but sustained his shoulder injury in a reserve team match against Aston Villa and spent the majority of the campaign in the treatment room. A recurrence of the problem following his return near the end of the season made it a year to forget for James, but he was battling back to full fitness again at the beginning of the 2007-08 campaign.

MAREK STECH

Czech under-17 goalkeeper who has been dubbed 'the new Petr Cech' in his homeland. Recommended to the Club by goalkeeping coach Ludek Miklosko, the 17-year-old has made a big impression since arriving at Upton Park in August 2006.

He joined Sparta Prague as a trainee in July 2005 before moving to West Ham United a year later, and made his first appearance for the under-18s in a 0-0 draw with Chelsea.

Marek has represented the Czech Republic at under-17 level and was a member of the silver-medal winning Czech Republic team that reached the final of the UEFA under-17 Championships in May 2006. He also represented the Czech Republic in the UEFA Under 17 Football Championships in 2007.

Youth Academy Membership

How to apply for your official club membership:

The Academy (Adult category)

By telephone -	Call 0870 112 2700*
Online -	Visit www.whufc.com (Tickets & membership section)
In Person -	Visit the stadium ticket office* or alternatively our store in Lakeside
Postal applications -	Print the PDF application form on the website (at the top of the blue column on the right), complete and send to: Membership applications, PO Box 4183, Manchester, M60 3AG

* Mon to Fri 9am to 5pm - Sat 9am to 1pm

West Ham United is pleased to offer our young supporters an exciting new membership package for the 2007-08 season.

For supporters aged from 0 to 15 - £25.00

Benefits include:

- Welcome pack including exclusive presentation box, kitbag & flag.

- Pre match e-newsletter

- Ticket priority

- Exclusive member's area of www.whufc.com

- Amazing shop offers & discount

- 3 Month WHUTV Subscription

Date of birth must be on or after 01/09/91

Due to requiring proof of identification, applications for both the Senior & Young Adult membership can only be accepted either via personal or by postal application

Hammers Legends

Bobby Moore
1958-1975
544 appearances, 24 goals

Trevor Brooking
1967-1984
528 appearances, 88 goals

Billy Bonds
1967-1988
655 appearances, 48 goals

Geoff Hurst
1959-1972
411 appearances, 180 goals

Alan Devonshire
1976-90
358 appearances, 29 goals

Tony Cottee
1983-88, 1994-97
280 appearances, 116 goals

Alvin Martin
1977-1997
469 appearances, 27 goals

Martin Peters
1959-1970
302 appearances, 81 goals

Paolo Di Canio
1999-2003
118 appearances, 47 goals

Freddie Ljungberg

Spot the difference

![Spot the difference photo with circled differences]

Who Am I Quiz

?

1. Scott Parker
2. Danny Gabbidon
3. Bobby Zamora

2006-07 Quiz

1. **Bobby Zamora**
2. **Palermo**
3. **1-2**
4. **Marlon Harewood**
5. **Manchester United**
6. **Brighton & Hove Albion**
7. **Lucas Neill**
8. **Kepa Blanco**
9. **Seven**
10. **Luis Boa Morte**
11. **Carlos Tevez (2), Mark Noble**
12. **Green, Neill, Ferdinand, Collins, McCartney, Benayoun, Noble, Reo-Coker, Boa Morte, Zamora, Tevez**

Wordsearch

```
F R Y W N B F A K A T E Y D F C E R
G F Q Z A M O R A B E L L O M O D O
I N E R E E F U O I E R S V U L C M
B R O R G R E E N O T S F E A L O A
R T I B R L M B G B R C A R B I I S
D F I O L O O E G C D O U T B N K N
T F G I L E S R E D G R B S I S I I
I D H P L M P Y Y S G E E O O I L L
S Z L T E Y U T N E I L L N J G L L
D S F A S H T O N S R E L V G D F O
E C E W I C D Z N E Y Y A G U I A A
G S R S N I N A T T U T M D E I U R
J D L C B I O M R Y D X Y A R H B F
L F L B L L T S U P S O N W O R E B
S P A R K E R O A F D S R S A E R R
D G O B E I H N C D F S A U I S T T
F Y M G R L S M C C A R T N E Y D F
F A H A E J A A R G D S U Y I R D A
```

61